School Sta

Maths Skills

Scholastic Children's Books,
Euston House, 24 Eversholt Street,
London NW1 1DB, UK

A division of Scholastic Ltd
London ~ New York ~ Toronto ~ Sydney ~ Auckland
Mexico City ~ New Delhi ~ Hong Kong

Published in the UK by Scholastic Ltd, 2016

Text by Chris Baker
Illustrations by Lee Robinson

ISBN 978 1407 16393 2

Printed and bound by Thumbprints, Malaysia

2 4 6 8 10 9 7 5 3 1

scholastic.co.uk

Guide for Parents

This book will help your child learn and practise the key maths concepts that are usually taught in Year 1 and into Year 2. This is the time when children need to learn basic but vital maths concepts. Children become familiar with numbers written in different ways, for example in numerals or words. They learn to use numbers to put things in order, and to count and measure. They learn to use numbers for comparing, such as 'longer' and 'shorter', and for calculations. Meanwhile they begin to study geometry – the maths of shapes.

This book covers a wide range of material from Key Stage 1, so please be aware that it may include things that your child has not yet done at school.

Children vary a lot in how quickly they grasp maths concepts and children who take longer aren't necessarily less intelligent. It is important to work at a speed that is right for your child. In particular, try to avoid a 'cycle of failure'. This can happen when a child cannot do something and becomes anxious, frustrated or ashamed. These bad feelings make it harder to think or concentrate, so things keep getting worse. It is much better to work out what the problem is calmly and then fix it.

In the middle of this book you will find game cards, which can be used to practise maths by playing and doing puzzles. This is as important a way of learning as doing the exercises in the book because your child will be practising maths while having fun! When you play the games, encourage your child to think ahead. This practises the important numeracy skill of thinking logically.

You can help your child by:

- Providing a good environment in which to work, with few distractions.

- Stopping if your child is tired or frustrated.

- Switching between different activities and games.

- Noticing what works for your child and doing more of that. Some children like doing the exercises, others will prefer the games.

- Using maths with your child in everyday activities:
  - Counting, measuring and calculating, for example when shopping or cooking.
  - Thinking about shapes, for example in craft projects or DIY.
  - In games: many traditional card, dice or boxed games use numbers.
  - When travelling, for example counting the steps on a walk.

- Praising effort as well as results. This can be crucial to encourage children who are slightly slower learners.

Fill in the gaps in this table to show each number as numerals, words and dots.

Numerals	Words	Dots
1		●
	Two	● ●
3		● ● ●
4	Four	
	Five	● ● ● ● ●
6		● ● ● ● ● ●
7	Seven	
	Eight	● ● ● ● ● ● ● ●
9		● ● ● ● ● ● ● ● ●
10	Ten	
11		● ● ● ● ● ● ● ● ● ● ●
	Twelve	● ● ● ● ● ● ● ● ● ● ● ●
13	Thirteen	

Numerals	Words	Dots
14		● ● ● ● ● ● ● ● ● ● ● ● ● ●
	Fifteen	● ● ● ● ● ● ● ● ● ● ● ● ● ● ●
16		● ● ● ● ● ● ● ● ● ● ● ● ● ● ● ●
	Seventeen	● ● ● ● ● ● ● ● ● ● ● ● ● ● ● ● ●
18	Eighteen	
19		● ● ● ● ● ● ● ● ● ● ● ● ● ● ● ● ● ● ●
	Twenty	● ● ● ● ● ● ● ● ● ● ● ● ● ● ● ● ● ● ● ●

Blast Off!

Can you count down from 10 so the rocket can blast off?

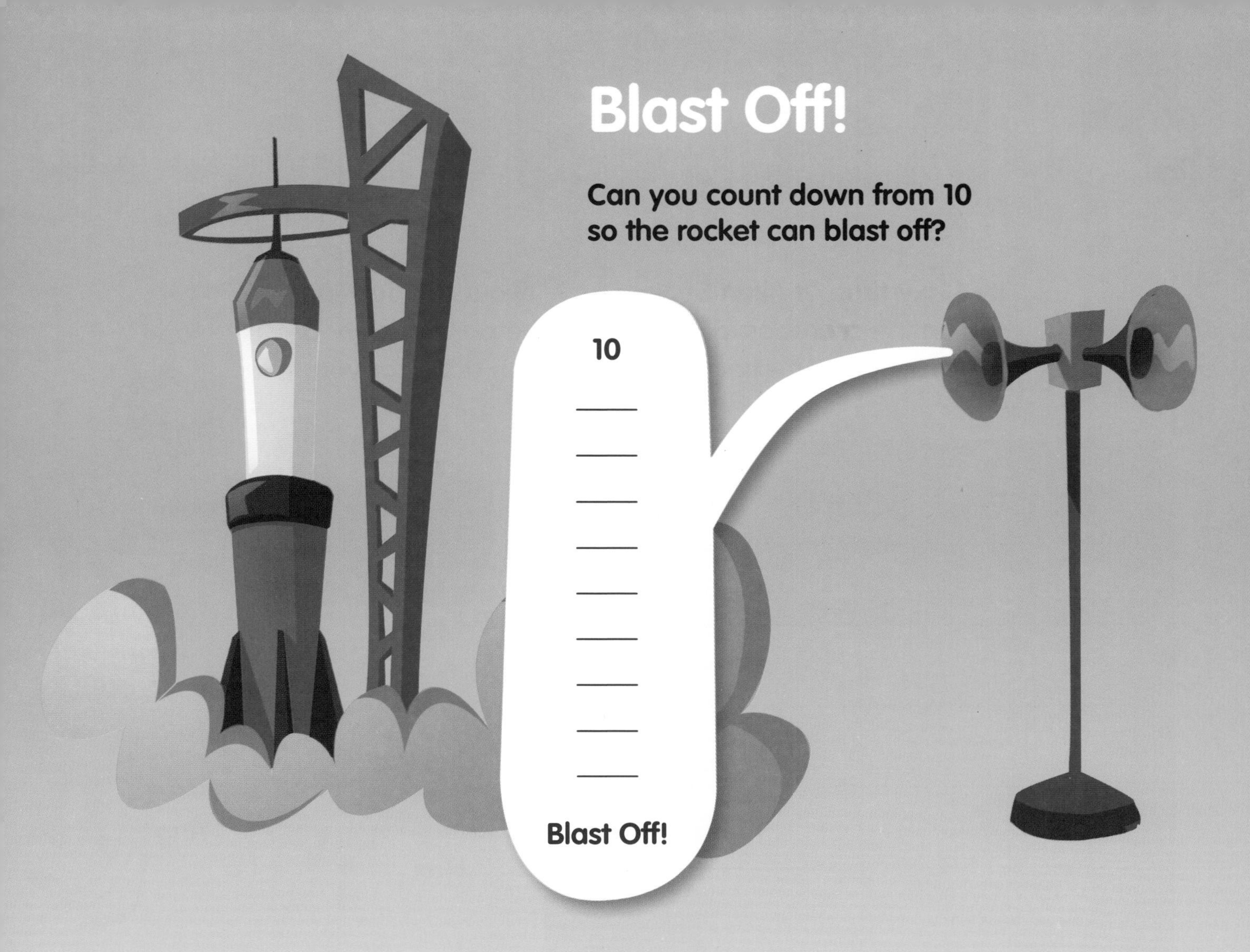

Alien Sports Day

Six players are needed for a game of Flong. Are there enough players here? If not, draw the extra players needed.

Position and Order

It's prize time at Alien Sports Day! Fill out the positions on the scoreboard. Then write the positions on the rosettes. The first ones have been done for you.

Name	Score	Position
Nong	12	
Ting	15	
Wek	20	1st
Blum	13	
Hox	9	
Goopy	5	
Grap	18	2nd
Jisp	7	
Konk	16	
Yatti	1	

Konk

Planet Hop

Draw a safe path for the rocket. It has to visit the planets in order, starting with the smallest number on its journey home.

Number Maze

Find and colour a path across the number maze. Move one square at a time in any direction. Always move to the LARGEST number you can. The first ones have been done for you.

START	5	12	20	99	8	3	66	83	38
20	25	30	15	1	17	4	12	10	23
3	7	36	29	67	24	65	68	70	73
26	33	40	30	17	21	63	8	57	75
34	39	47	50	53	55	60	56	45	77
86	6	30	22	5	44	13	4	64	80
13	88	29	34	17	81	52	11	28	82
99	24	32	100	6	26	39	41	58	85
22	91	51	13	1	18	72	58	15	90
75	8	28	48	74	10	4	29	5	HOME

Fill in the gaps in the calculations below.
You can use the number line to help you.

5 + 4 = 9

4 + 3 = __	7 + 2 = __	10 + 5 = __
3 + __ = 7	6 + __ = 9	12 + __ = 15
__ + 5 = 8	__ + 9 = 10	__ + 14 = 20

STAR TIP!
For additions like __ + 3 = 6, find 3 and 6 on the number line. The answer is the number of jumps between them.

Maths Machines

This machine adds **3** to any number put into it.
Fill in the missing numbers.

This machine adds **5** to any number put into it.
Fill in the missing numbers.

Subtraction

Fill in the gaps in the calculations below.
You can use the number line to help you.

8 – 2 = 6

9 – 2 = ___	6 – 1 = ___	16 – 4 = ___
5 – ___ = 2	8 – ___ = 7	15 – ___ = 12
___ – 10 = 2	___ – 8 = 12	___ – 16 = 1

STAR TIP!

For subtractions like ___ – 10 = 2, ask yourself 'what is 2 more than 10?'

Maths Machines

This machine subtracts 3 from any number put into it.
Fill in the missing numbers.

This machine subtracts 5 from any number put into it.
Fill in the missing numbers.

More Addition and Subtraction

To open the spaceship door you need to enter a number code.
Find the code by doing these calculations.
The first one has been done for you.

2 + 6 = 8

5 + 4 = ____

8 + 1 = ____

3 + 5 = ____

Follow the Leader to 10

Circle the rockets that belong with Squadron Leader 10.
If they belong, they show a calculation that equals 10.

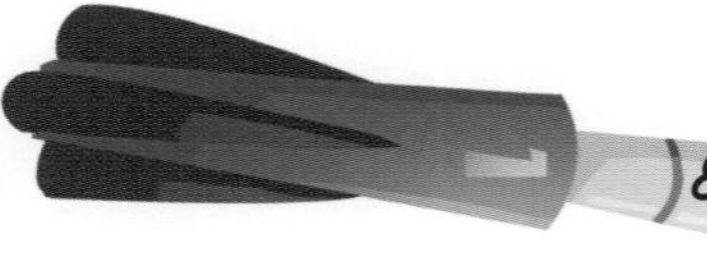

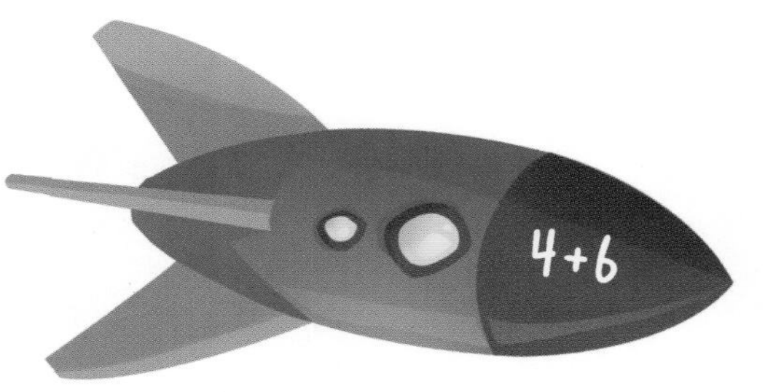

Through the Stars

Do the additions and subtractions below to work out the right path to guide the rocket through the stars. Then draw a line to show the route the rocket will take.

1 4 + 2	2 6 + 4	3 11 − 2	4 15 + 5	5 14 − 2
6 18 + 1	7 5 − 1	8 13 + 5	9 20 − 5	10 1 + 7

Follow the Leader to 20

Circle the rockets that belong with Squadron Leader 20. If they belong, they show a calculation that equals 20.

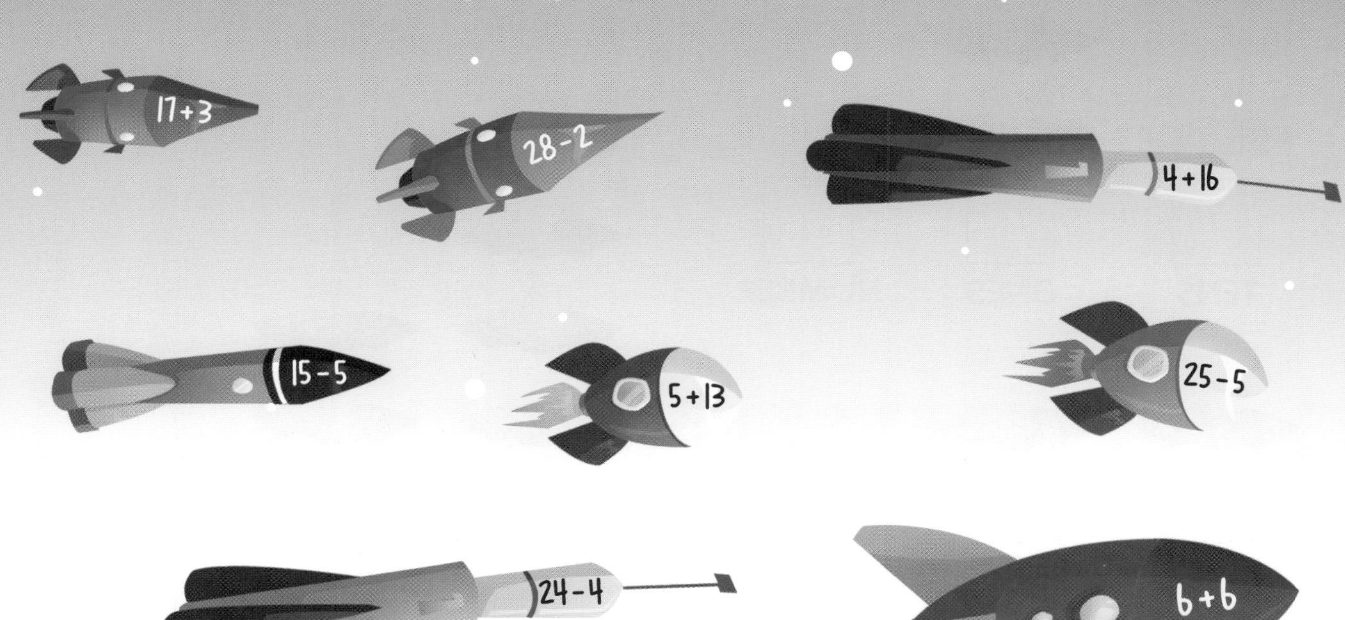

The alien stunt team pile up their flying saucers to show the tens and ones of a two-digit number. Write the numbers they have made. The first one has been done for you.

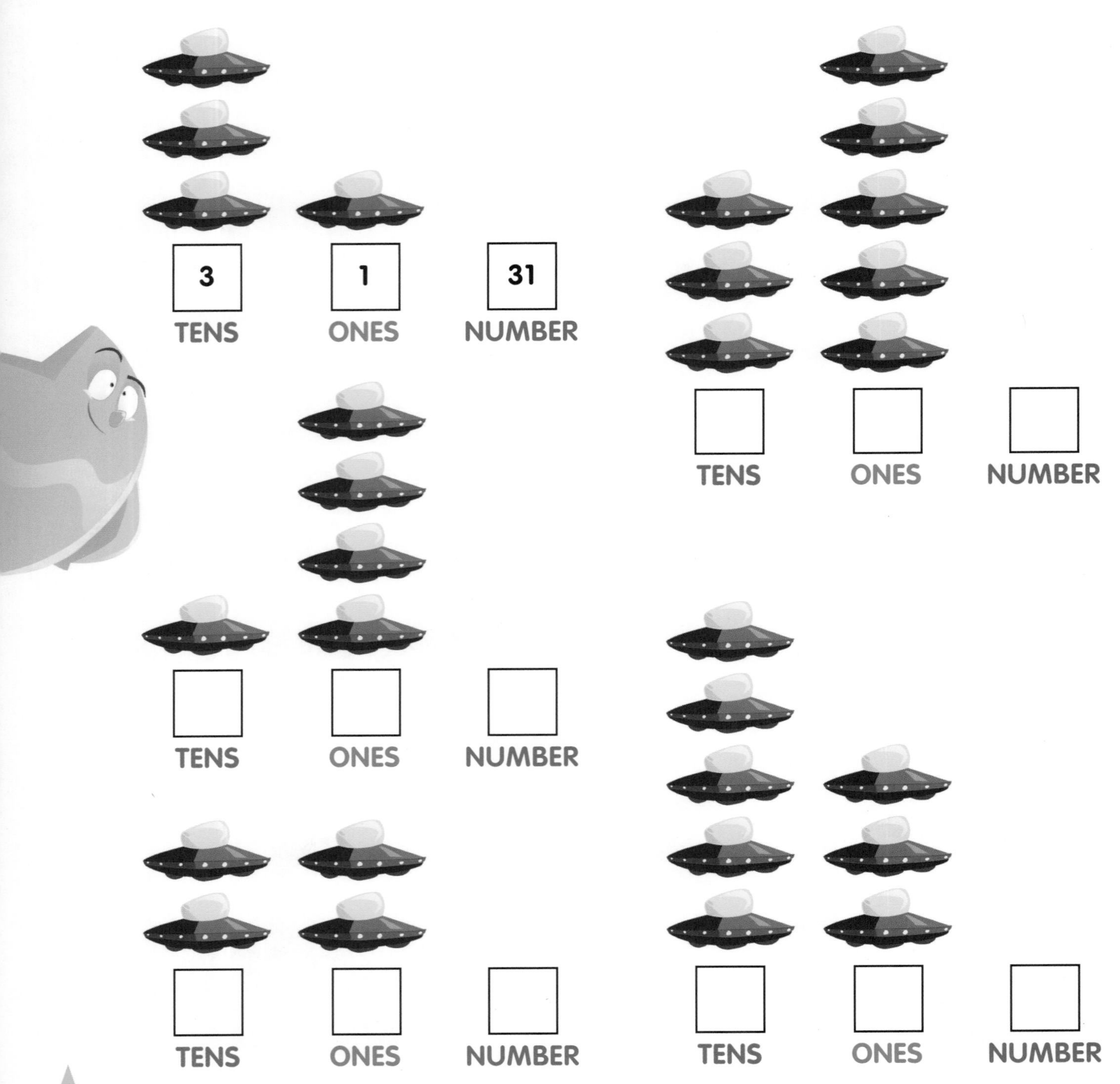

Alien Stunt Team

Colour in the right number of flying saucers in the tens and ones columns to show the numbers below. Then fill in the numbers in the boxes below.

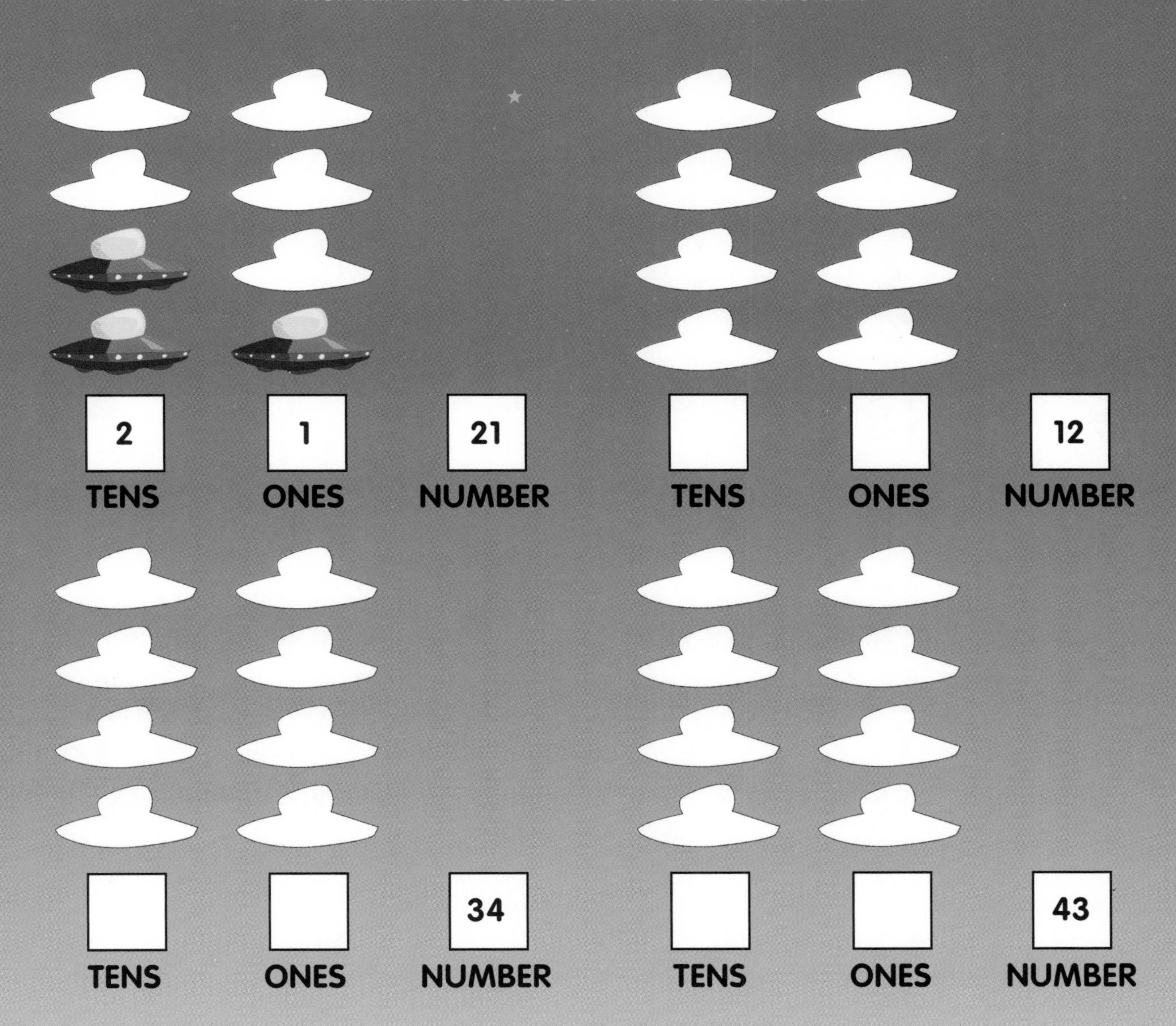

Look at the numbers on pages 14 and 15.
What is the LARGEST number the stunt team has made?

What is the SMALLEST number the stunt team has made?

Look at these rockets, then answer the questions below.

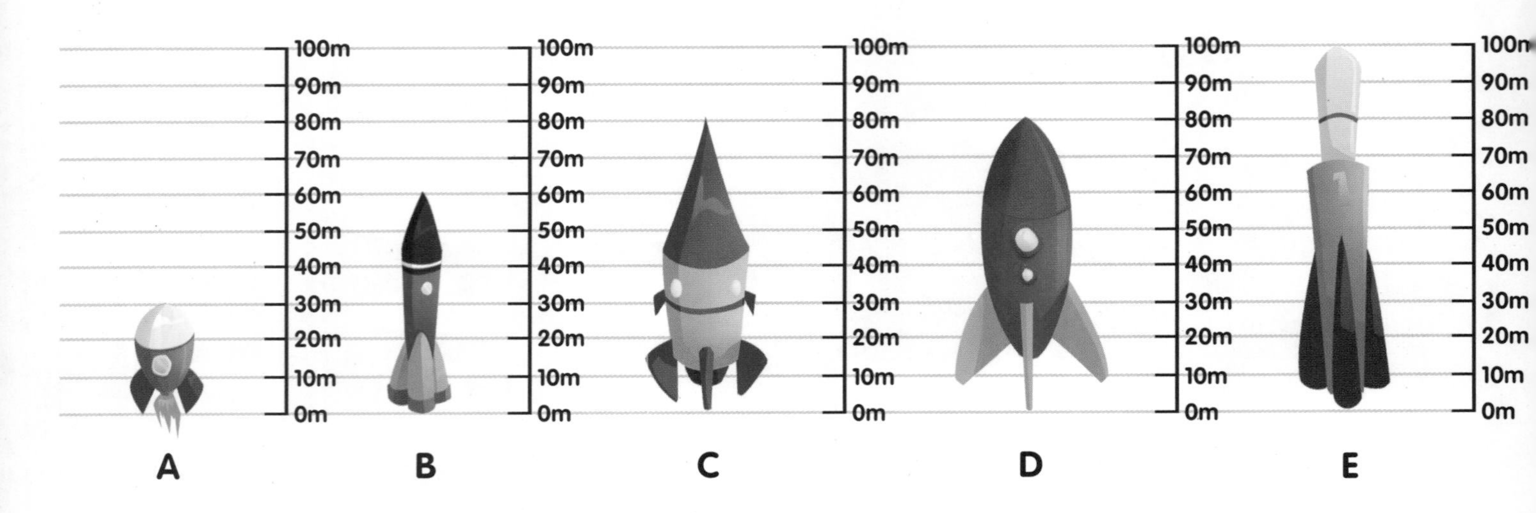

Questions:

1. How tall is rocket B? __________
2. Which rocket is the tallest? __________
3. Which rocket is the shortest? __________
4. Is rocket A taller or shorter than rocket C? __________
5. Which rocket is half as tall as rocket B? __________
6. Which rocket is double the height of rocket A? __________
7. Which two rockets are the same height? __________

STAR TIP!
You can use your length rods from the middle of this book to play more games about comparing lengths.

3 5 6 6

3 4 5 6

3 4 5 6

3 4 5 6

2 4 5 6

2 4 5 6

Six	Six	Five	One	Four	One	2	
Five	Zero	Four	Three	Three	Three	1	•
Four	Three	Three	Five	Two	Six	1	
Three	Five	Two	Four	One	Two	0	
Two	Four	One	Two	Zero		Six	Two
One	Four	Zero		Six	Six	Five	Five

TANGRAM PUZZLE

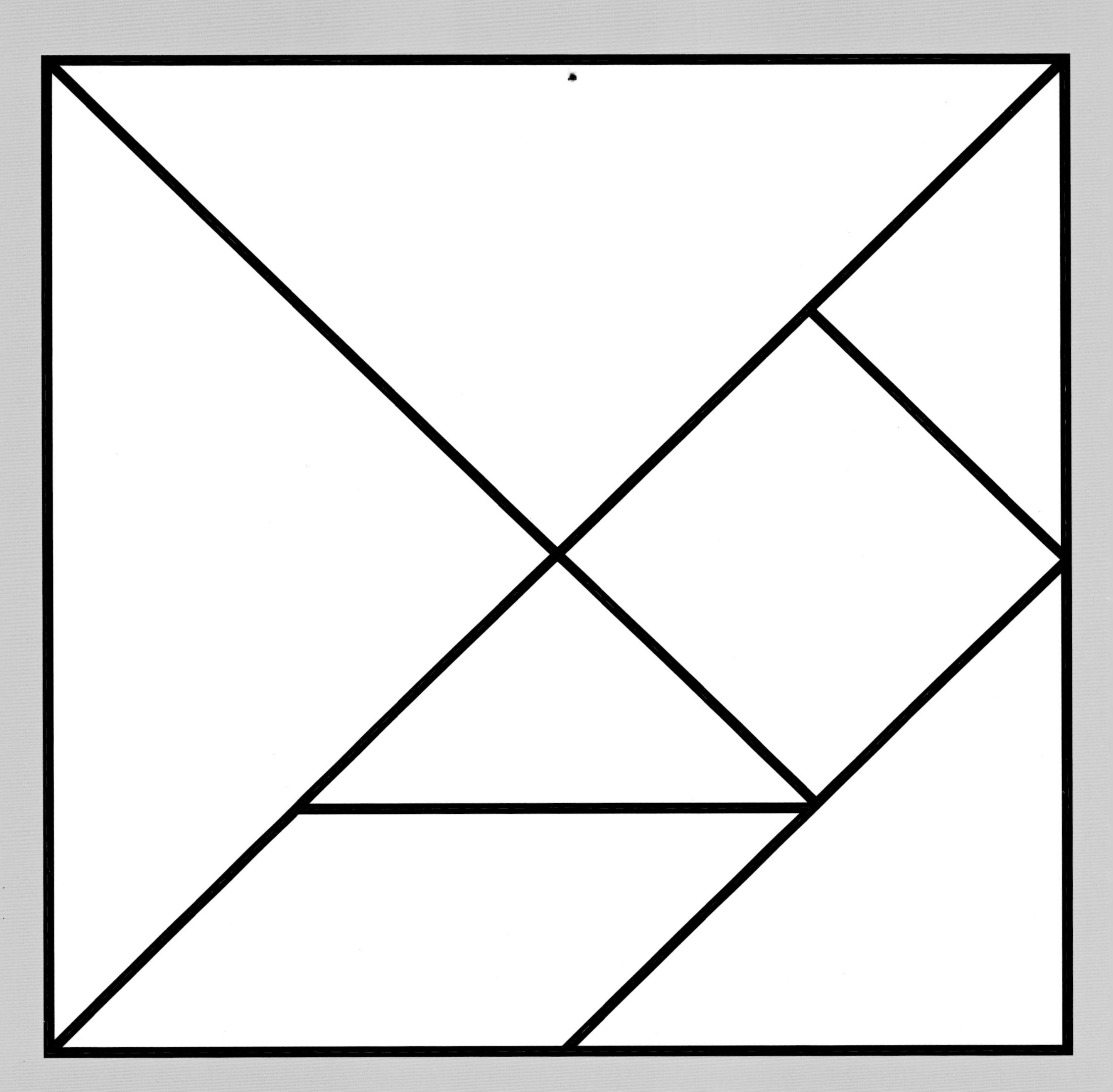

Push out a set of triangles and quadrilaterals.

1 2

3 4

5 6

7

8 9

10 10

9 8

7

6 5

4 3

2 1

Push out this set of 20 card strips of different lengths.

Alien See-Saw

Look at these aliens on see-saws and compare their weights.
First circle the heavier alien, then draw an alien friend next to the lighter alien. Give the new alien the right weight to make the see-saw balance.
The first one has been done for you.

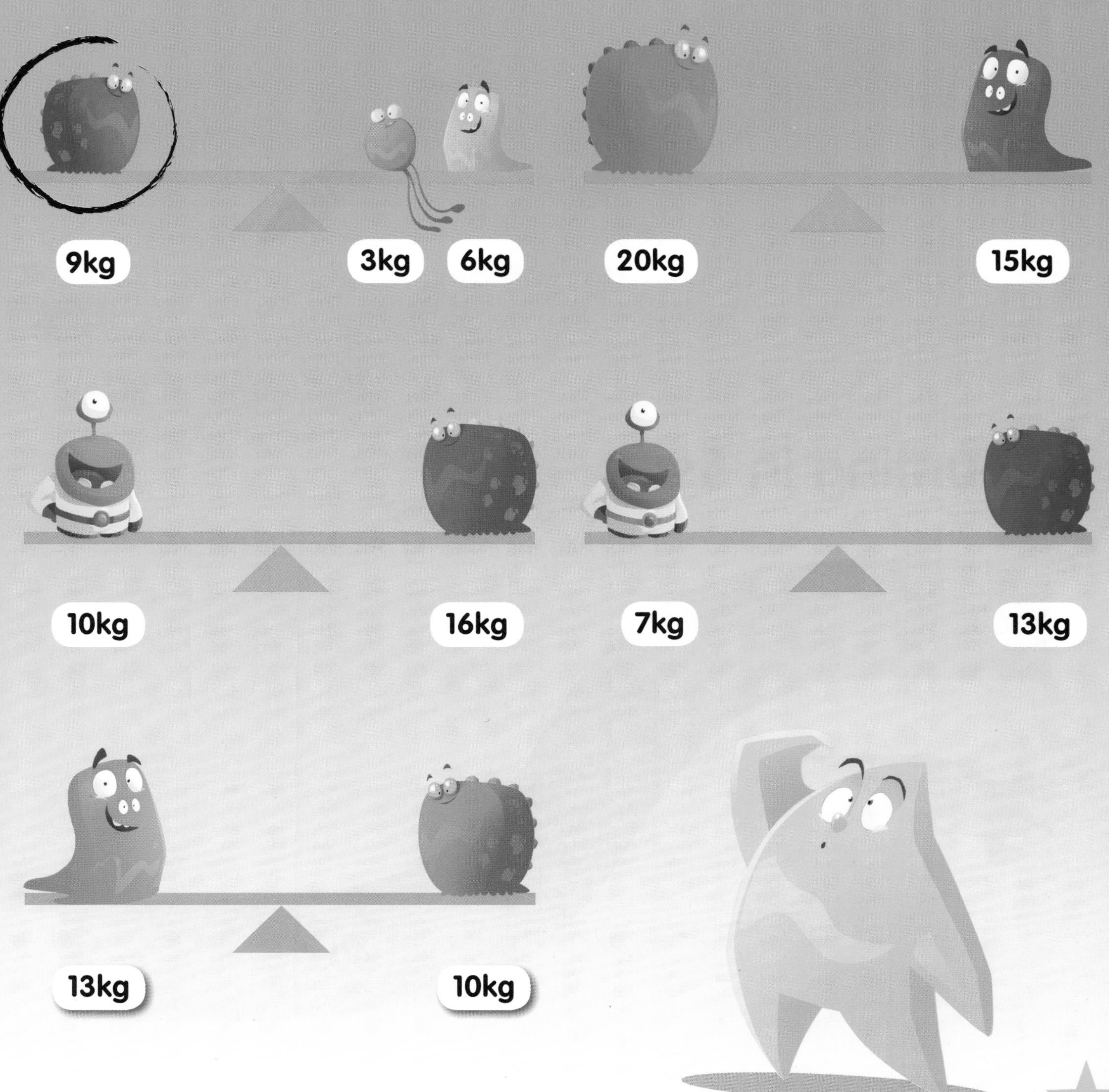

Counting in 2s

Let's count in twos!
Write the missing numbers in the stars.

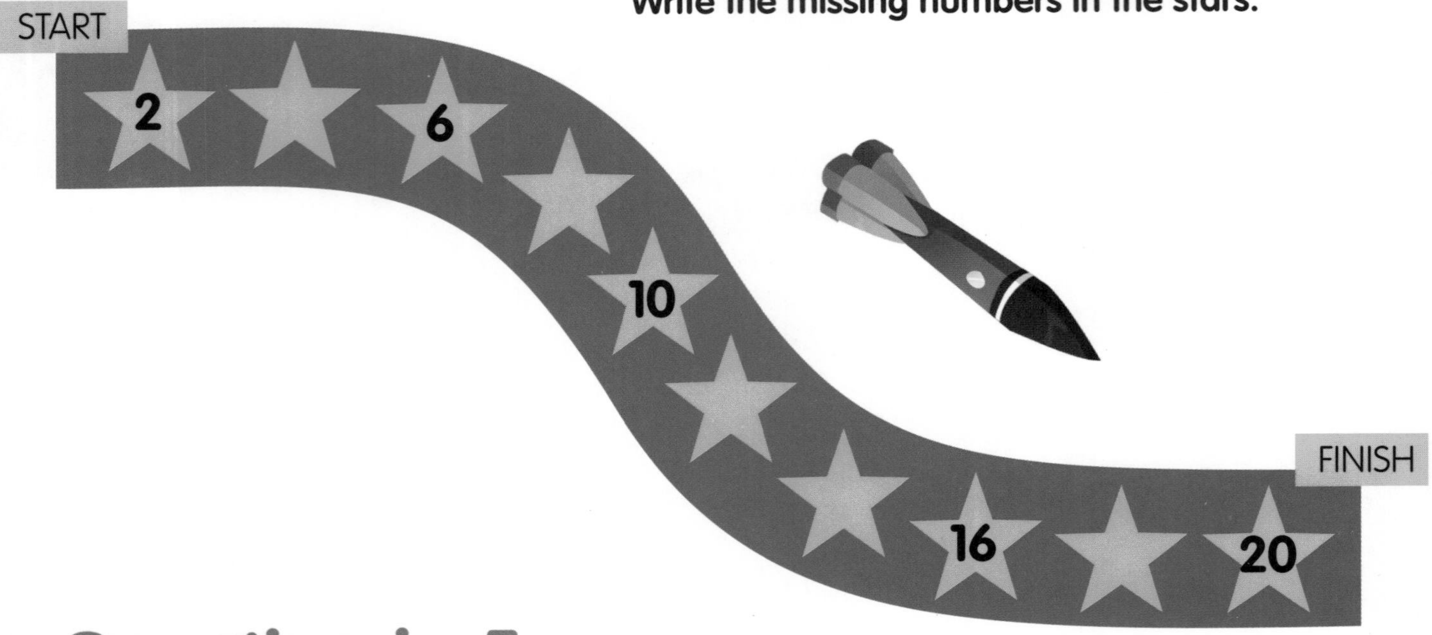

Counting in 5s

Let's count in fives!
Write the missing numbers in the stars.

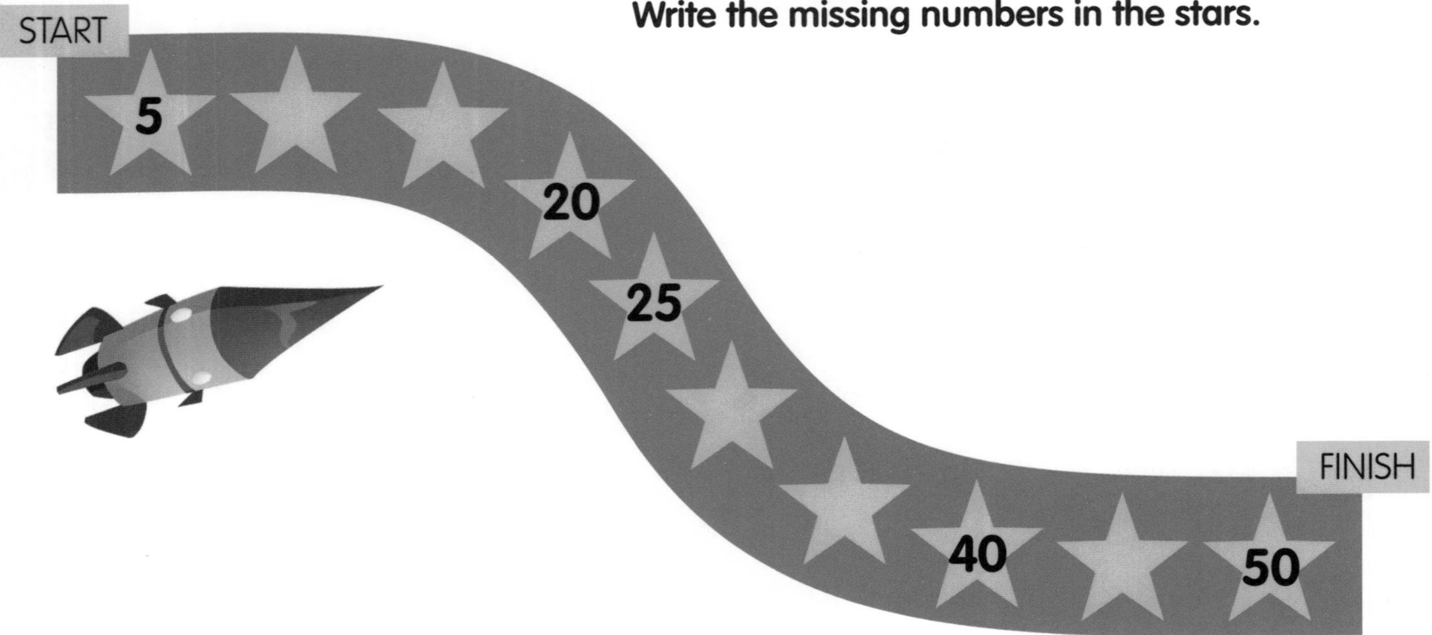

Counting in 10s

Let's count in tens!
Write the missing numbers in the stars.

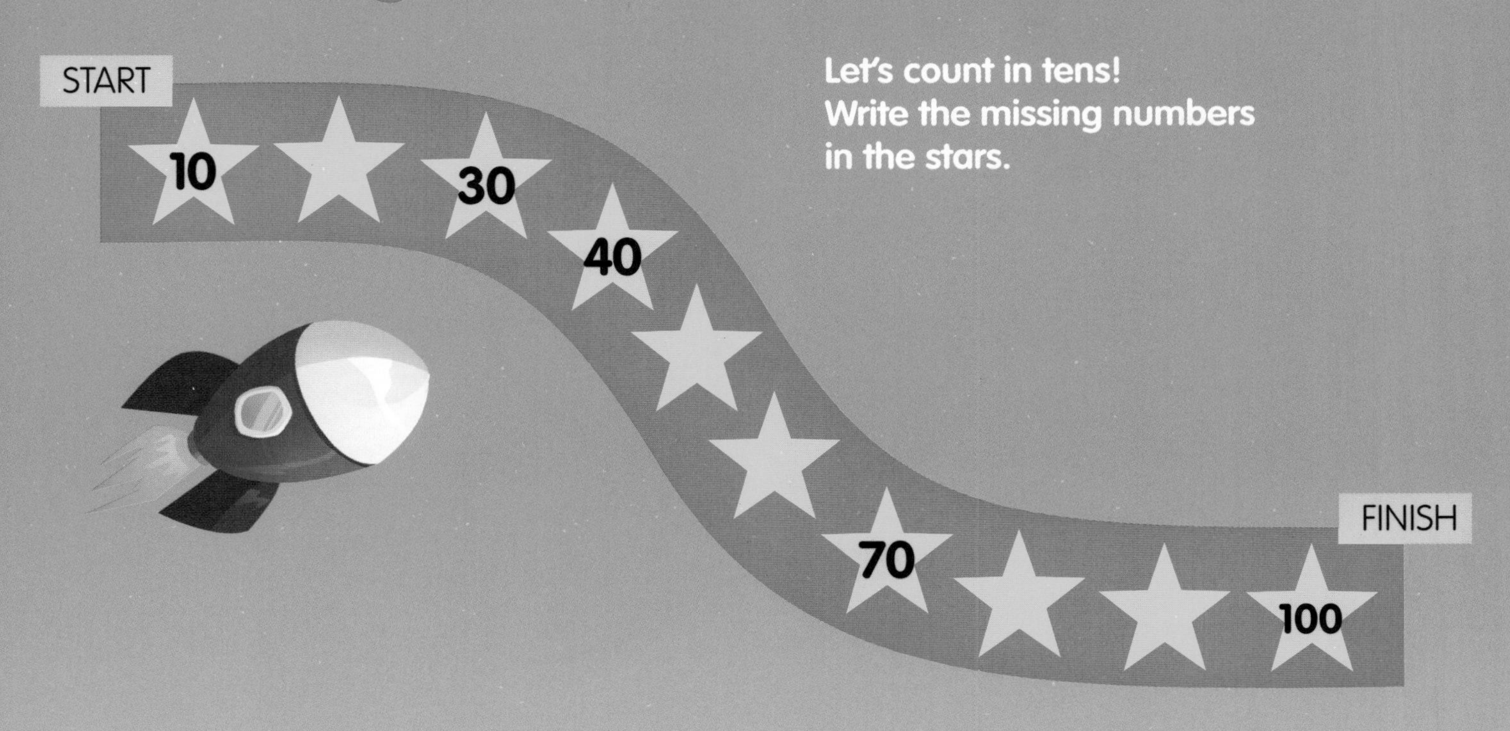

Journey Through Space

Draw a path for the rocket counting in twos. Then use another colour to draw a path for the rocket counting in fives. Finally use a third colour to draw a path for the rocket counting in tens.

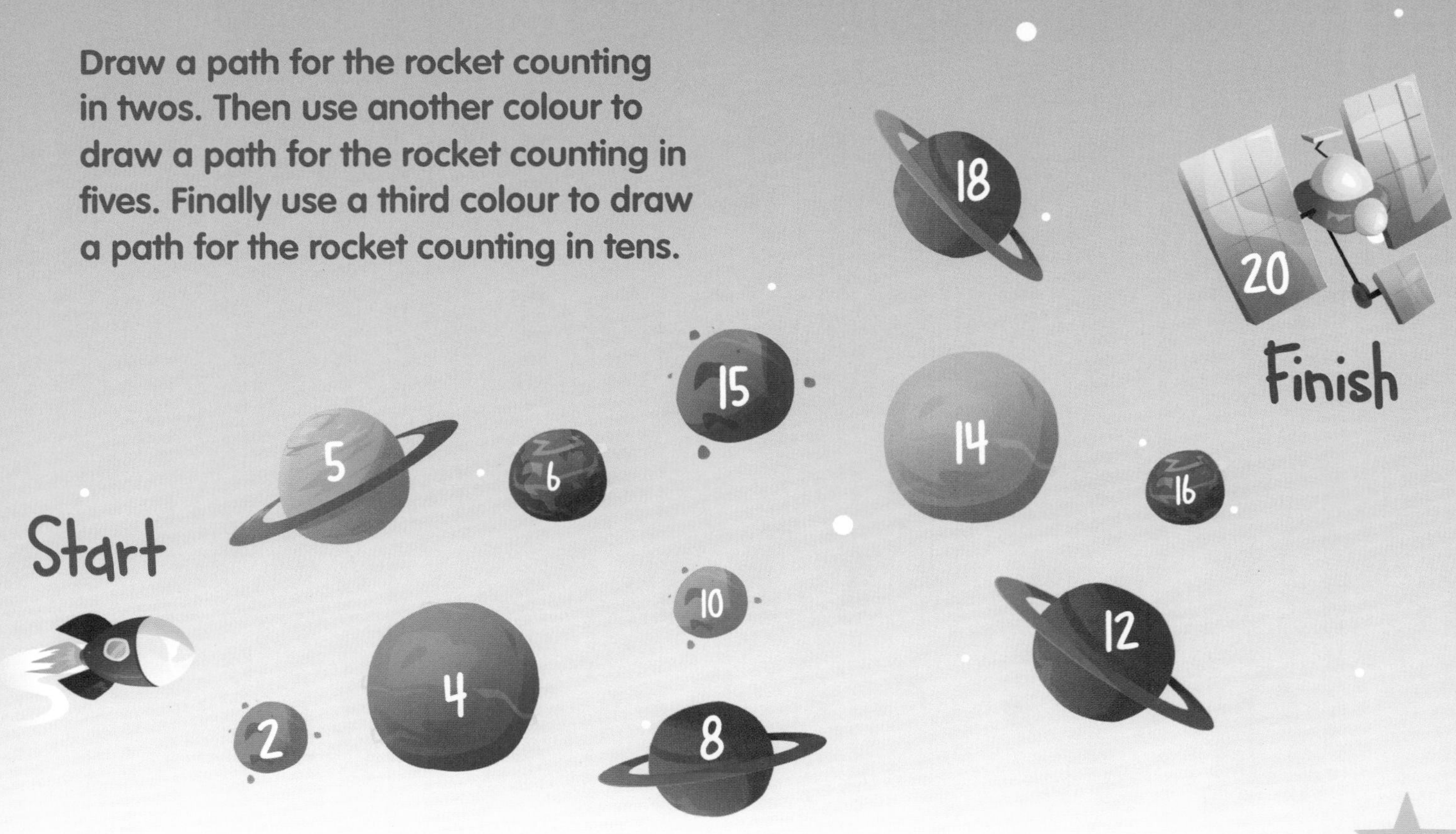

Multiplying and Dividing

Star has five points.

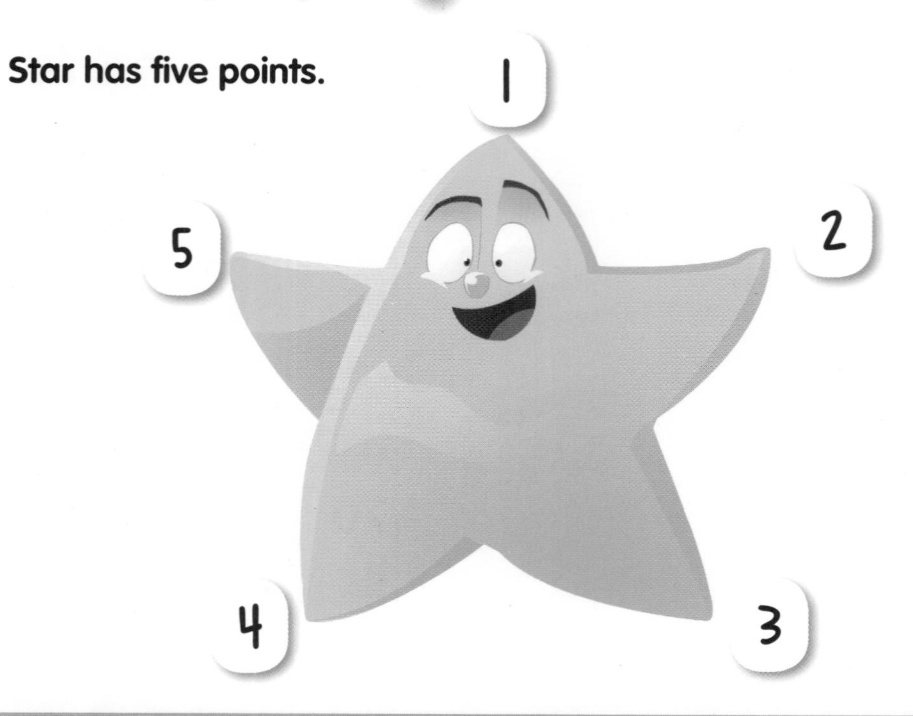

How many points in total do these groups of stars have? Write the calculation. The first one has been done for you.

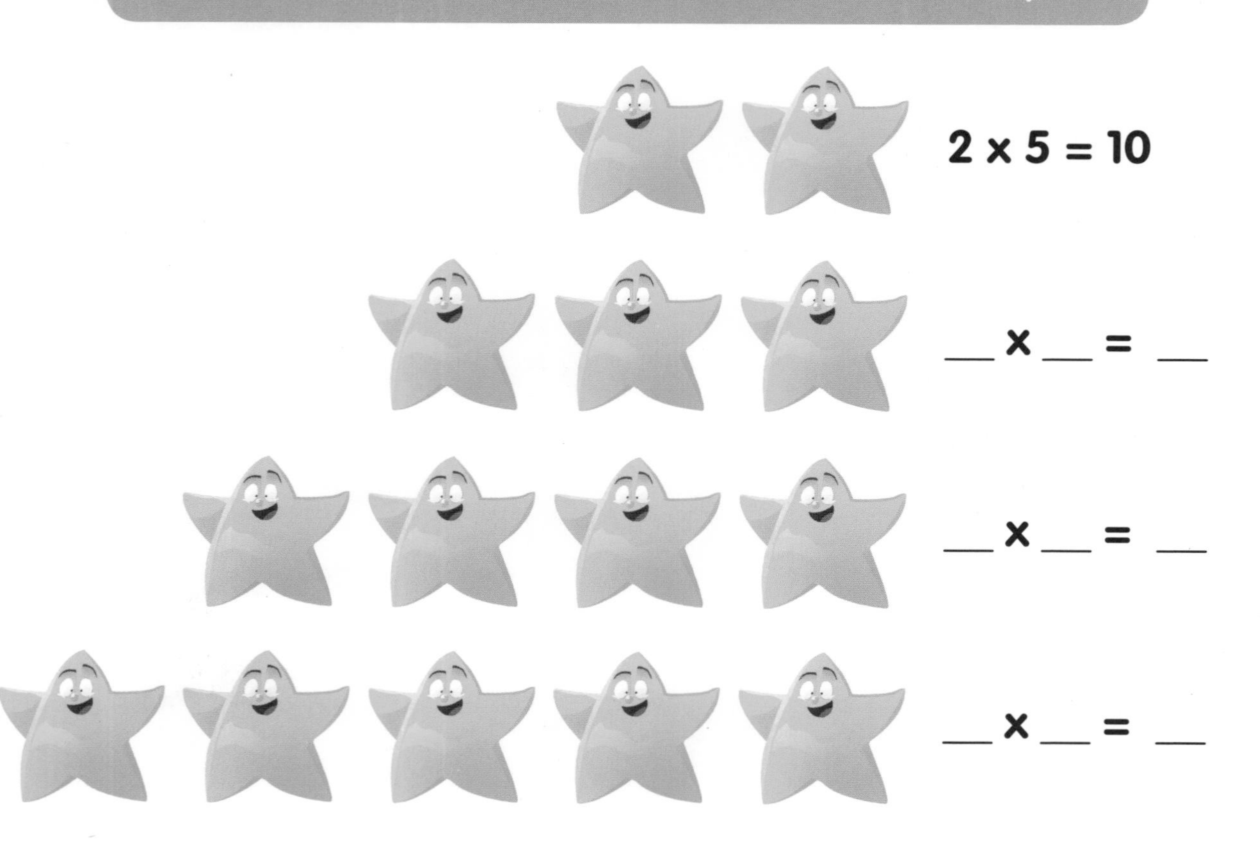

2 x 5 = 10

__ x __ = __

__ x __ = __

__ x __ = __

How Many Feelers?

This alien has two feelers.
How many feelers in total do these groups have? Write the calculations.

STAR TIP!
Can you do this by counting in twos, or using the two times table?

1 x 2 = 2

__ x __ = __

__ x __ = __

__ x __ = __

Alien Crowd

**These aliens are watching a football match.
Can you answer the questions on the opposite page?**

	COLUMN 1	COLUMN 2	COLUMN 3	COLUMN 4	COLUMN 5
ROW 1					
ROW 2					
ROW 3					
ROW 4					

Questions:

1. How many aliens are there in each row? ____

2. How many aliens are there in each column? ____

3. How many rows are there? ____

4. How many columns are there? ____

5. How many aliens are there in total? ____

6. Multiply the number of rows by the number of columns.

   Write the calculation. ____ x ____ = ____

7. How many aliens are there in 3 rows? Write the calculation.

   ____ x ____ = ____

8. How many aliens are there in 2 rows? ____ x ____ = ____

9. Draw a box around half of the aliens in the crowd.

Fractions

Two aliens want equal parts of this pizza.
Colour in how much one alien gets.

What fraction of the pizza does each alien get? ____________

Four aliens want equal parts of this pizza.
Colour in how much one alien gets.

What fraction of the pizza does each alien get? ____________

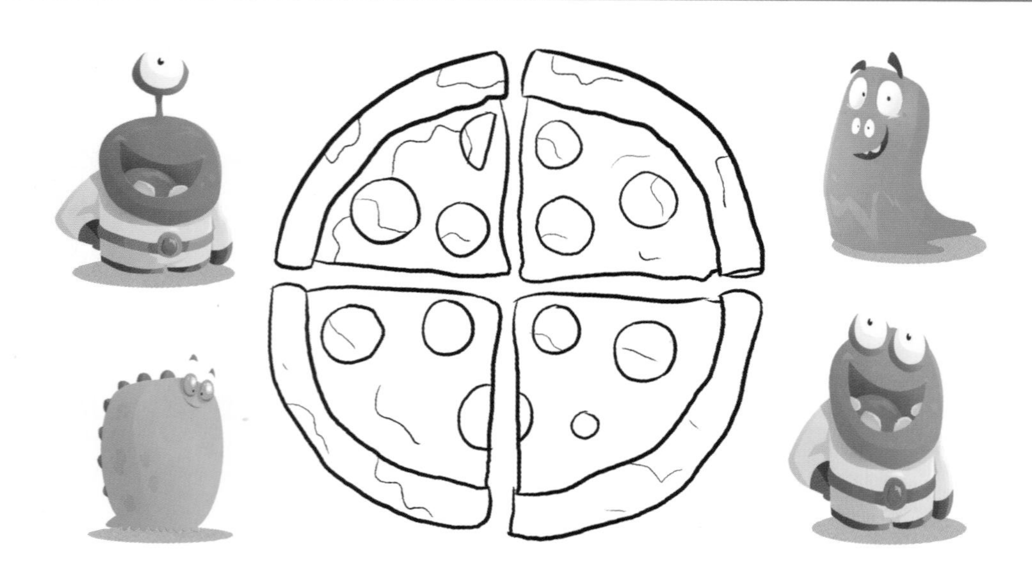

Rocket Parts

Look at these rockets, then complete the tasks below.

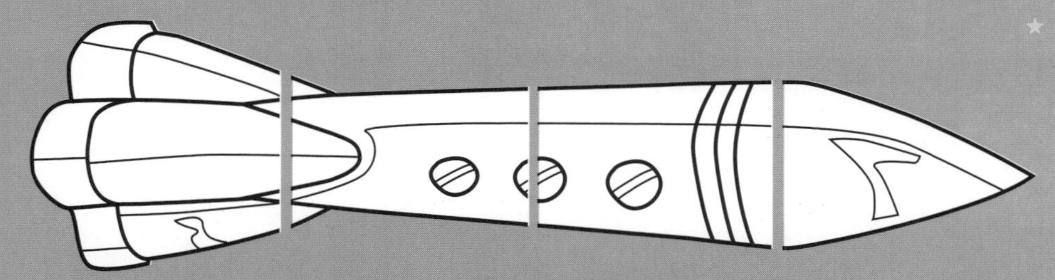

1. Colour in ¼ of the rocket.

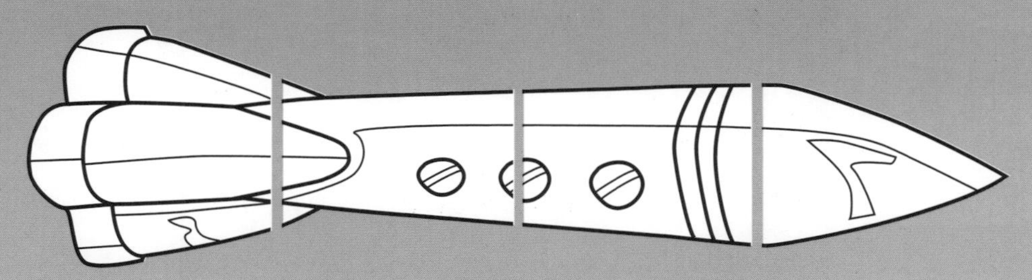

2. Colour in ½ of the rocket.

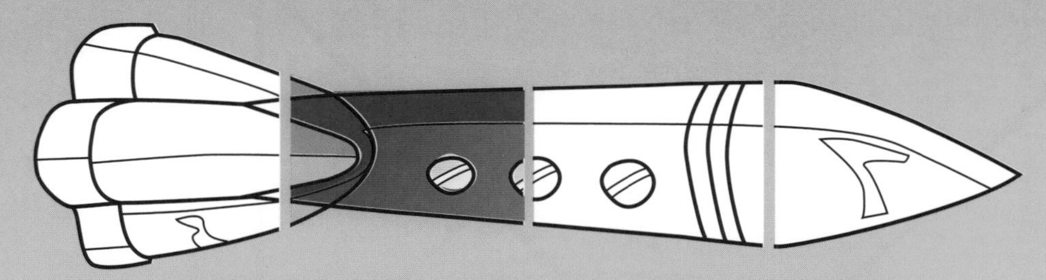

3. What fraction of this rocket is coloured in?

____

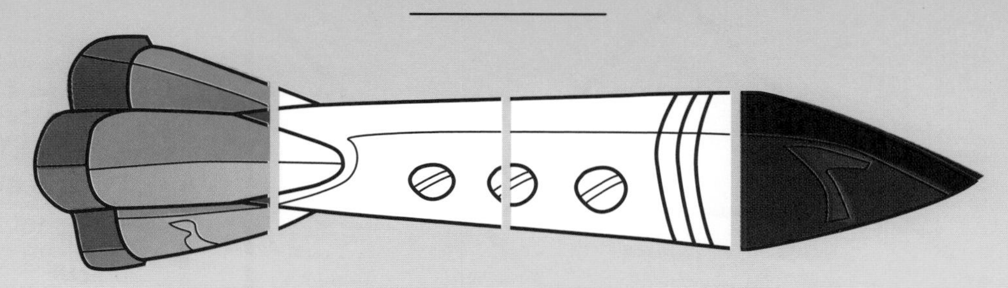

4. What fraction of this rocket is coloured in?

____

Look at the shapes below, then complete the sentences.

This is a ______________________ .

It has ______ corners and ______ edges.

This is a ______________________ .

It has ______ corners and ______ edges.

This is a ______________________ .

It has ______ corners and ______ edges.

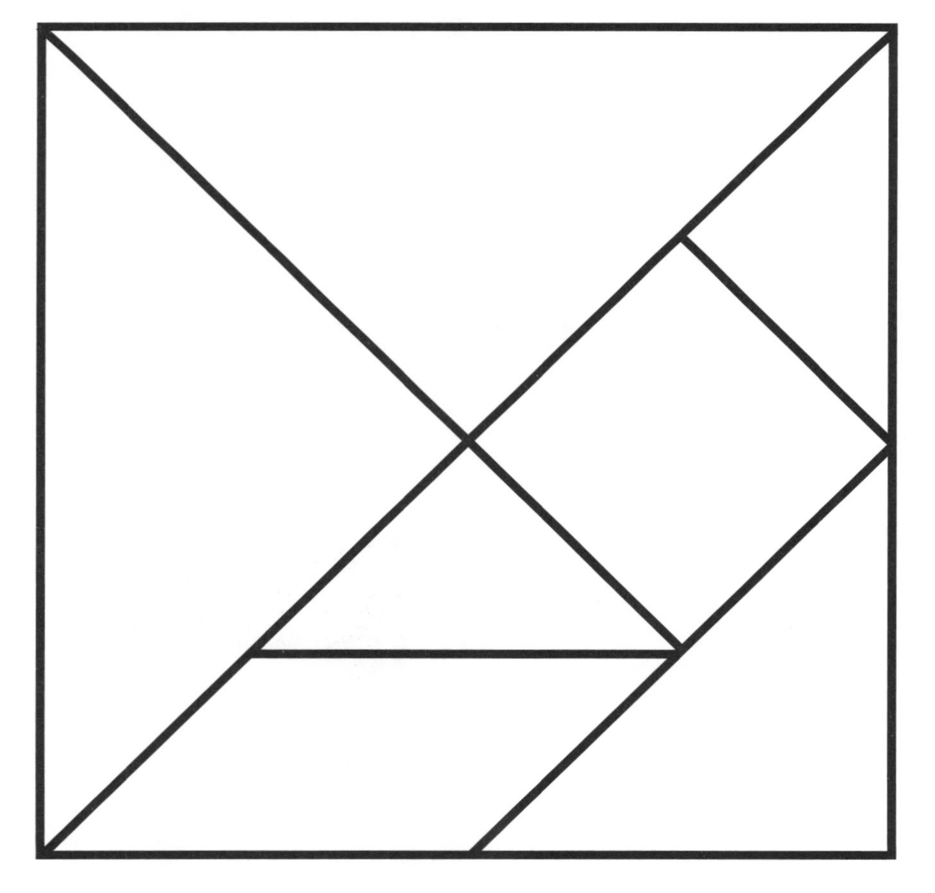

Colour the triangles in this picture in different colours. How many triangles are there in total?

There are ____ triangles.

STAR TIP!

You can use the tangram set in the middle of this book for sorting and counting the pieces, as well as playing the tangram game.

Draw Your Own Spaceship

Design your own awesome shapeship below! You must make the spaceship using only triangles, circles and four-sided shapes.

3-D Spaceship

This spaceship is made from different 3-D shapes. Draw an arrow from each of the shapes to the word that describes it.

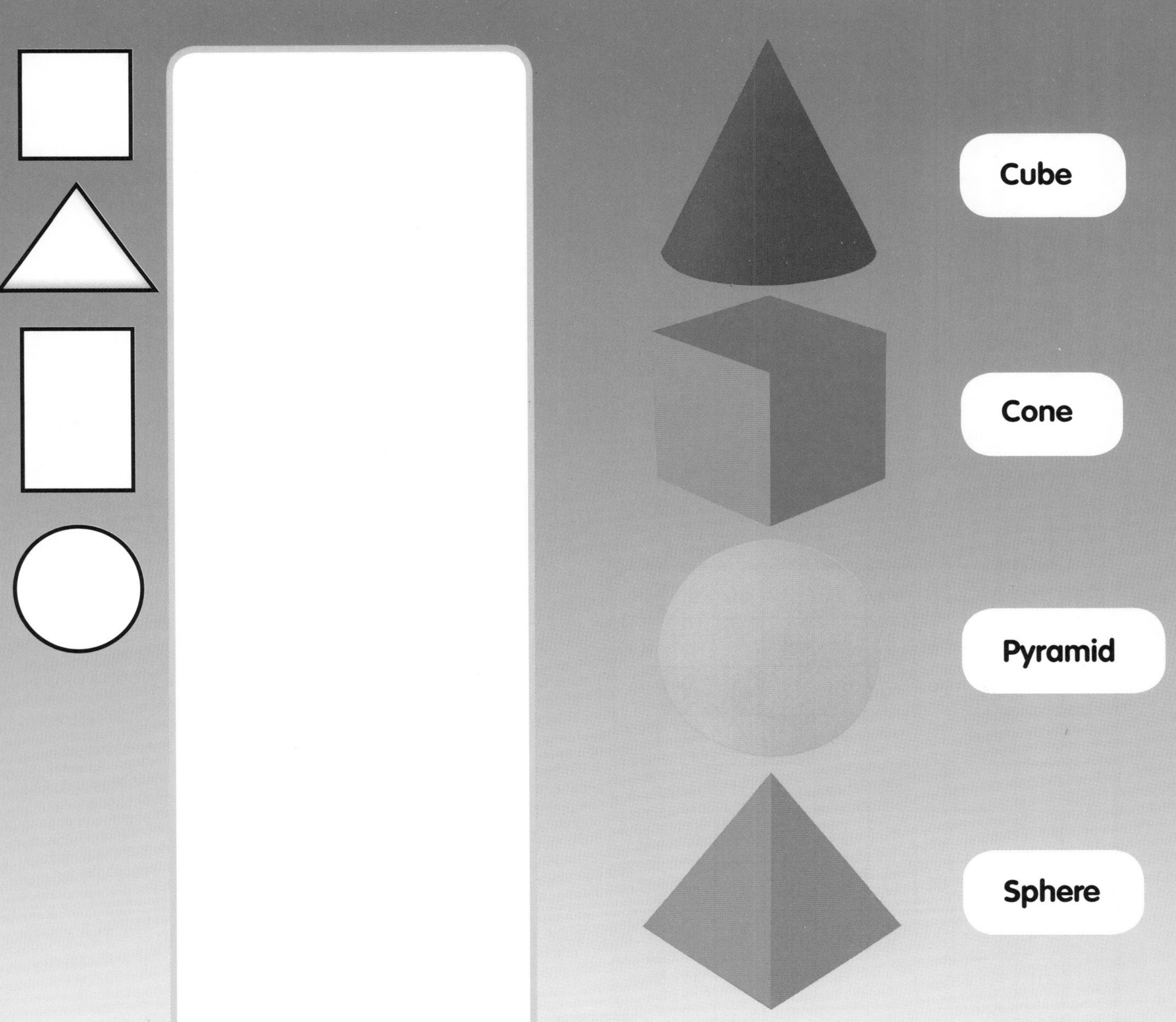

The Answers

Page 5

Alien Sports Day

There should be 3 extra players.

Page 6

Position and Order

The aliens came in the following positions:

Nong	6th	Goopy	9th
Ting	4th	Grap	2nd
Wek	1st	Jisp	8th
Blum	5th	Konk	3rd
Hox	7th	Yatti	10th

Page 7

Planet Hop

The rocket should hop to 3, 11, 22, 30, 35, 41, 46, 59, 64, 68, 82, 89, 93 and 99.

Number Maze

START	5	12	20	99	8	3	66	83	38
20	25	30	15	1	17	4	12	10	23
3	7	36	29	67	24	65	68	70	73
26	33	40	30	17	21	63	8	57	75
34	39	47	50	53	55	60	56	45	77
86	6	30	22	5	44	13	4	64	80
13	88	29	34	17	81	52	11	28	82
99	24	32	100	6	26	39	41	58	85
22	91	51	13	1	18	72	58	15	90
75	8	28	48	74	10	4	29	5	HOME

Page 9

Maths Machines

+3: the missing numbers are (from top to bottom) 6, 9, 12, 18 and 14.
+5: the missing numbers are (from top to bottom) 5, 11, 2, 17 and 14.

Page 11

Maths Machines

–3: the missing numbers are (from top to bottom) 7, 10, 4, 9 and 14.
–5: the missing numbers are (from top to bottom) 10, 10, 15, 17 and 14.

Page 12

Spaceship Door Code

The door code is 8998.

Follow the Leader to 10

The rockets that belong with Squadron Leader 10 are: 8+2, 4+6, 15–5 and 18–8.

Page 13

Through the Stars

The route is: 6, 10, 9, 20, 12, 19, 4, 18, 15 and 8.

Follow the Leader to 20

The rockets that belong with Squadron Leader 20 are: 17+3, 24–4, 4+16 and 25–5.

Pages 14 and 15

Alien Stunt Team

The numbers are (from left to right, top to bottom): 35, 14, 22 and 53.
The largest number is 53. The smallest number is 12.

Page 16

Measuring

1. Rocket B is 60m.
2. Rocket E is the tallest.
3. Rocket A is the smallest.
4. Rocket A is shorter than rocket C.
5. Rocket A is half as tall as rocket B.
6. Rocket B is double the height of A.
7. Rockets C and D are the same height.

Page 17

Alien See-Saw

The missing aliens weigh (from left to right, top to bottom): 5kg, 6kg, 6kg and 3kg.

Page 19

Journey Through Space

Counting in twos, the rocket will visit 2, 4, 6, 8, 10, 12, 14, 16, 18 and 20.
Counting in fives, the rocket will visit 5, 10, 15 and 20.
Counting in tens, the rocket will visit 10 and 20.

Page 20

Multiplying and Dividing

The calculations are:
$3\times5=15$
$4\times5=20$
$5\times5=25$

Page 21

How Many Feelers?

The calculations are:
$2\times2=4$
$3\times2=6$
$4\times2=8$

Page 23

Alien Crowd

1. There are 5 aliens in each row.
2. There are 4 aliens in each column.
3. and 4. There are 4 rows and 5 columns.
5. There are 20 aliens in total.
6. $4\times5=20$
7. There are 15 aliens in 3 rows: $3\times5=15$
8. There are 10 aliens in 2 rows: $2\times5=10$

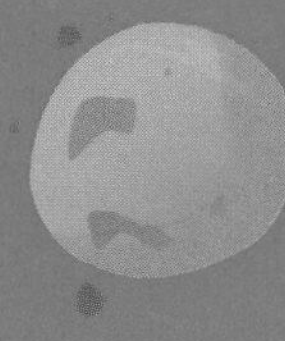

Page 24

Fractions

Two aliens get ½ of the pizza each.
Four aliens get ¼ of the pizza each.

Page 25

Rocket Parts

3. ¼ of the rocket is coloured in.
4. ½ of the rocket is coloured in.

Page 26

Shapes

The square has 4 corners and 4 edges.
The triangle has 3 corners and 3 edges.
The rectangle has 4 corners and 4 edges.

There are 5 triangles in the picture altogether, or 6 if you put the two big triangles together!

Page 27

Use Your Game Cards To...

1. Sort numbers

Press out the domino cards. Use the cards to practise recognizing numbers when they are shown in different ways. Using only the numbers on the left side of each card, sort them in order from smallest to largest.

2. Play Block Dominoes

Game for 2–4 players.

How to Play:

- Each player picks up eight dominoes. The rest of the dominoes are left face down in a pile in the middle.
- The first player places one of their dominoes face up.
- If the next player has a domino that matches a number on the first domino, he or she places it on the table face up, so that the matching numbers touch.
- The numbers may be in words, as a numeral or as dots.

- All these different ways of showing the number 'match' if it is the same number, for example the word 'six' matches numeral 6 or six dots. Two dominoes have the Magic Star symbol. This matches anything! (If you have a star domino it's good to keep it for a time when none of your normal dominoes match.)
- If the next player has a domino that matches, they can add another domino so that a line slowly builds up. Players can't build side branches (you can only match the ends of the line), but the line can turn a corner when you run out of space.
- If a player doesn't have a domino that matches, he or she can either take a domino from the middle, or if there are no dominoes left, the player misses their go.
- The winner is the first player to use up all their dominoes.

3. Play Tangrams

Game for 1 player.

How to Play:

- **Press out the tangram shapes.**
- **See if you can arrange the pieces to make shapes like these:**

What other pictures can you make? Make up your own, or you may be able to find other tangram puzzles in books or online. There are loads to choose from!

4. Play 'Just as Tall'

Game for 2 players.

How to Play:

- Press out all the length rods.
- Player 1 places any rod apart from the 1 rod on the table.
- Player 2 has to find as many ways as they can of making a set of rods the same length. For example, a 10 rod is just as tall as two 5 rods, or a 4 rod and a 6 rod, or two 4 rods and a 2 rod (which we often describe as 10 = 5 + 5, 10 = 4 + 6 and 10 = 4 + 4 + 2).

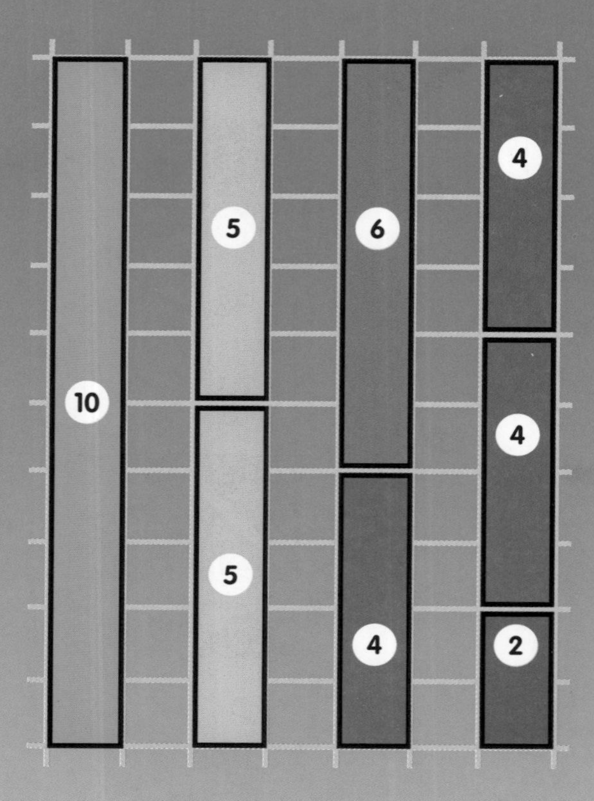

- Write down the number of different sets of rods that Player 2 found.
- Change players so that Player 2 chooses and places a rod on the table and Player 1 finds the largest number of sets possible.
- Repeat so each player chooses the rods five times.
- Add up each player's score, which is the number of sets they've found in total over the five games. The winner is the player with the highest score.